PUFFIN BOOKS

THE DINOSAUR'S DINNER

June Crebbin has been a primary school English teacher for most of her life, in both Leicestershire and Yorkshire. June began writing in 1971 while continuing part-time teaching, and looking after a young family. She took early retirement in December 1990, and continues to write widely for adults and children.

By the same author

Poetry:

THE JUNGLE SALE

Fiction:

FINDERS KEEPERS
RIDE TO THE RESCUE

June Crebbin

The Dinosaur's Dinner

Illustrated by Thelma Lambert

PUFFIN BOOKS

For the staff and pupils, past and present, of Birstall Highcliffe Primary School

PUFFIN BOOKS

Published by the Penguin Group
Penguin Books Ltd, 27 Wrights Lane, London W8 5TZ, England
Penguin Books USA Inc., 375 Hudson Street, New York, New York 10014, USA
Penguin Books Australia Ltd, Ringwood, Victoria, Australia
Penguin Books Canada Ltd, 10 Alcorn Avenue, Toronto, Ontario, Canada M4V 3B2
Penguin Books (NZ) Ltd, 182–190 Wairau Road, Auckland 10, New Zealand

Penguin Books Ltd, Registered Offices: Harmondsworth, Middlesex, England

First published by Viking 1992
Published in Puffin Books 1994
1 3 5 7 9 10 8 6 4 2

Printed in England by Clays Ltd, St Ives plc
Filmset in Baskerville

Contents

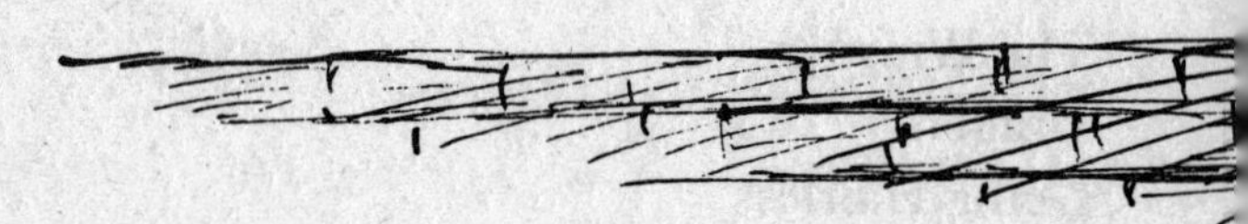

Warning to a Person Sitting Under an Apple Tree in an Autumn Garden on a Sunny Afternoon With Their Nose Stuck in a Good Book

Directly up above you hanging by a thread
An apple's getting ready to thump you on the
head.

The Secret

'Oh please oh please oh please,
What are we going to do?
Is it the seaside? Is it a park?
Is it a trip to the zoo?'

'It's our little secret,' said Grandad.
'Surprise, surprise,' said Gran.
'Now eat up your toast, we want to
  be off
By half past ten if we can.'

'Oh please oh please oh please,
Where are we going to go?
I know it's a secret, I won't tell a soul,
It's just that I want to know.'

'All in good time,' said Grandad.
'Not long to wait,' said Gran.
'We'll wash up the pots and get
  packing
And then we'll tell you the plan.'

'Get packing? Oh where are we going?
And what are we going to do?
Is it far? Is it near? Is it miles?
Couldn't you give me a clue?'

'A clue?' said Grandad. 'I wonder.'
'A house that keeps moving?' said Gran.
'A house that keeps moving,' said Grandad,
'And travels to where it began.'

'A house with windows and curtains.
But a house,' said Gran, 'that's afloat.'
'A house on a river,' said Grandad –
'I've got it. I've guessed – it's a BOAT!'

'A boat,' said Gran, 'that you cook in
Where you go for the weekend and stay,
A boat that you drive and you fish from –'
'Oh please, can we start straight away?'

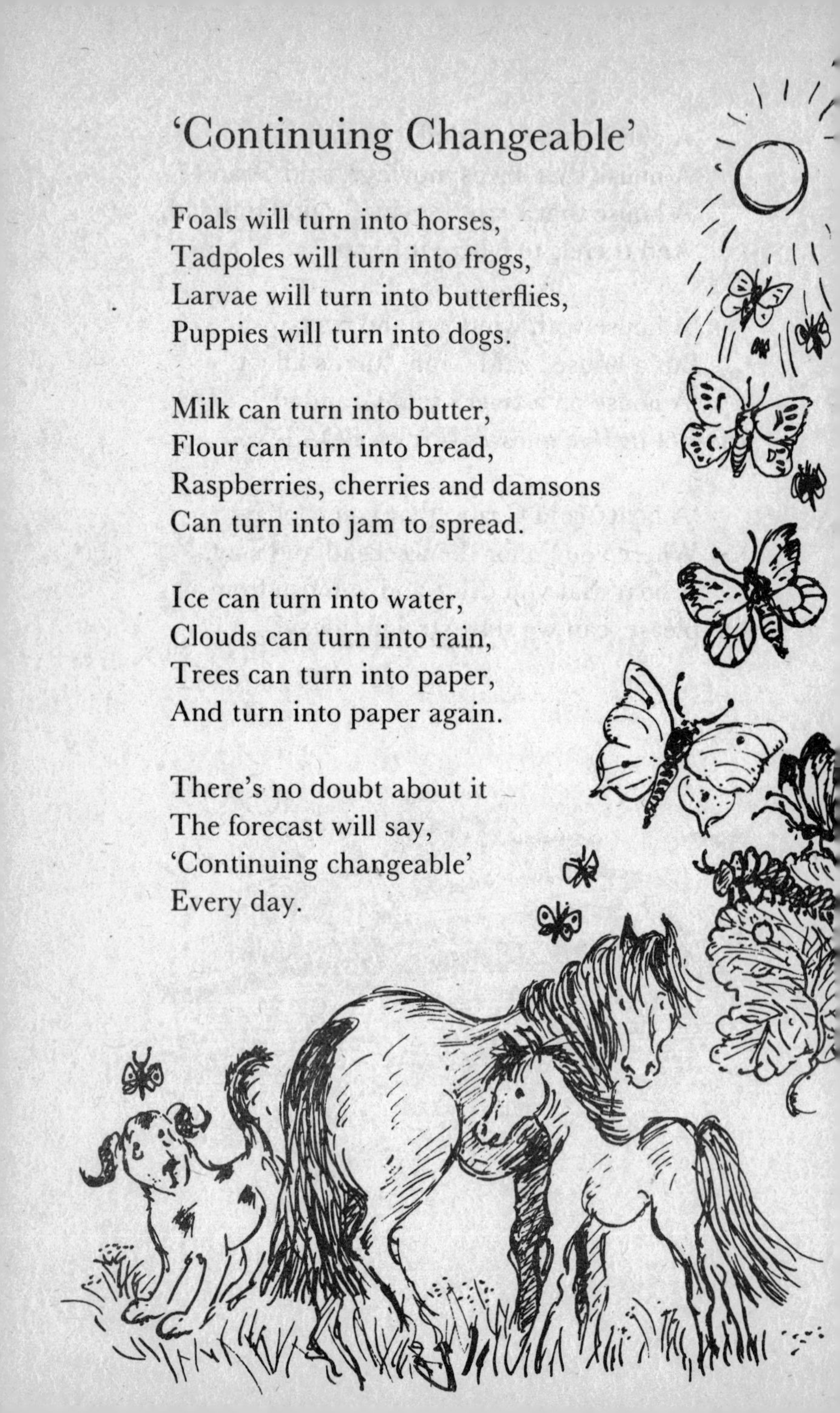

'Continuing Changeable'

Foals will turn into horses,
Tadpoles will turn into frogs,
Larvae will turn into butterflies,
Puppies will turn into dogs.

Milk can turn into butter,
Flour can turn into bread,
Raspberries, cherries and damsons
Can turn into jam to spread.

Ice can turn into water,
Clouds can turn into rain,
Trees can turn into paper,
And turn into paper again.

There's no doubt about it
The forecast will say,
'Continuing changeable'
Every day.

The Lolly's Last Request

I'M AN ICE-COLD LOLLY
WITH A JOKE UPON MY STICK
I'M A GETTING-WARMER LOLLY
WITH A DISAPPEARING TRICK
I'D RATHER DRIP INSIDE YOU
THAN BE A DRIP BESIDE YOU
SO PLEASE LICK ME QUICKLY
QUICKLY LICK ME
QUICKLY QUICKLY
LICK ME
LICK ME
LIC
L
L
!

The Dinosaur's Dinner

Once a mighty dinosaur
Came to dine with me,
He gobbled up the curtains
And swallowed our settee.

He didn't seem to fancy
Onion soup with crusty bread,
He much preferred the flavour
Of our furniture instead.

He ate up all our dining-chairs
And carpets from the floor,
He polished off the table, then
He looked around for more.

The television disappeared
In one almighty gulp,
Wardrobes, beds and bathroom
He crunched into a pulp.

He really loved the greenhouse,
He liked the garden shed,
He started on the chimney-pots
But then my mother said:

'Your friends are always welcome
To drop in for a bite,
But really this one seems to have
A giant appetite.

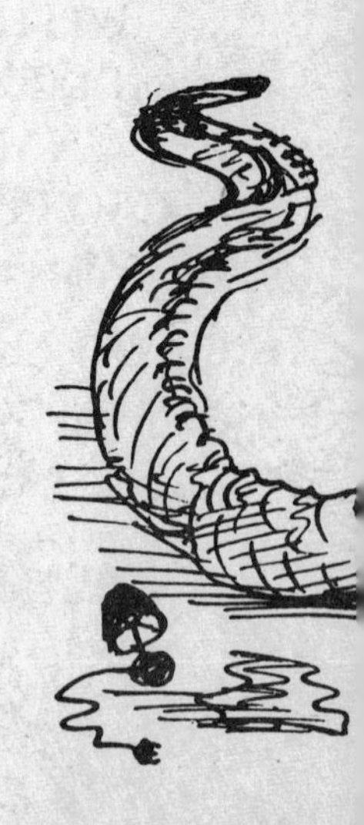

You'd better take him somewhere else,
I'm sure I don't know where,
I only know this friend of yours
Needs more than we can spare!'

And suddenly I realized
I knew the very place,
And when I showed him where it was
You should have seen his face –

I don't think I've seen anyone
Enjoy a dinner more,
I watched him wander on his way,
A happy dinosaur!

The council did rebuild our school,
But that of course took time . . .
And all because a dinosaur
Came home with me to dine!

Butterfly

This morning I found a butterfly
Against my bedroom wall.

I wanted to hold it,
To remember its colours.

But instead I guided its whirring shape
Towards the open window.

I watched it drift into the warm air,
Swaying and looping across the summer garden.

In my book I found:
'Tortoiseshell, reddish-orange with yellow
patches.'

But I remember its leaving,
And the pattern of its moving.

Bird-spotting

As I walked out one moonlit night
Under a starry sky,
I saw along a ghostly track
A crane come hurtling by:

'Coot! Coot!' it called as on it sped
So fast, so straight, so bright,
I thought that I had never seen
A more impressive kite.

As I walked on that moonlit night
Under a starry sky,
I saw two love-birds hand in hand
And heard one softly cry:

'O marry me, my starling,
I've been too long alone,
Come live with me and be my dove
In my ankestrel home.'

Snipe me! I thought. Can this be true?
And finched myself to see
If all that I had heard and seen
Was just imaginary . . .

So now wrenever larkness falls,
On brilliant moonlit nights,
I take a very pheasant stroll
In hope of wondrous kites.

The Whistler

My little brother is almost six,
He's good at maths and magic tricks,
He's quite a neat writer,
He can hop and jump and pull funny faces,
He can do top buttons and tie his laces,
He's a fearless fighter.

But he wanted to whistle – and though he tried
Till his face went red and he almost cried,
He still couldn't do it,
So he asked me how and I said: 'Make an O
With your mouth and then, very gently, blow
A whistle through it.'

And he did – but now the trouble is
My little brother practises
All day long,
He sucks in his cheeks, he puffs and blows,
Whatever he's doing, his whistling goes
On and on . . . and on . . .

Dragon

Beware, my teeth are like knives,
My claws sharper than needles,
My eyes colder than stone.

Fire roars out of my mouth,
Fierce tongues of flame
Seek out my enemy.

My tail will lash you to pieces,
My jaws will grind you to dust,
I am the Dragon of the Bedroom . . .

No you're not, Samantha,
I'm the dragon in this house,
Get your bedroom tidied up – or else!

Going Hairless

Oh, Dad, why did you do it?
It's just – you look so weird,
Your face looks sort of lonely
Without its fuzzy beard.

I liked your face as it was, Dad,
I liked it covered in hair,
I liked your chin all bristly
Not pink and bald and bare.

Why did you shave it off, Dad?
It doesn't look like you,
Your lips look sort of worried
And not sure what to do.

I'll miss your tickly beard, Dad,
When you come to say goodnight,
I'll miss the way that it prickles
Whenever we have a fight.

My friends all liked your beard, Dad,
I know they'll miss it too,
I'm not sure that they'll recognize
That you are really you.

I bet if you started today, Dad,
It wouldn't take long, I'm sure,
For your beard to be back to normal,
And you'd be my dad once more.

Spider

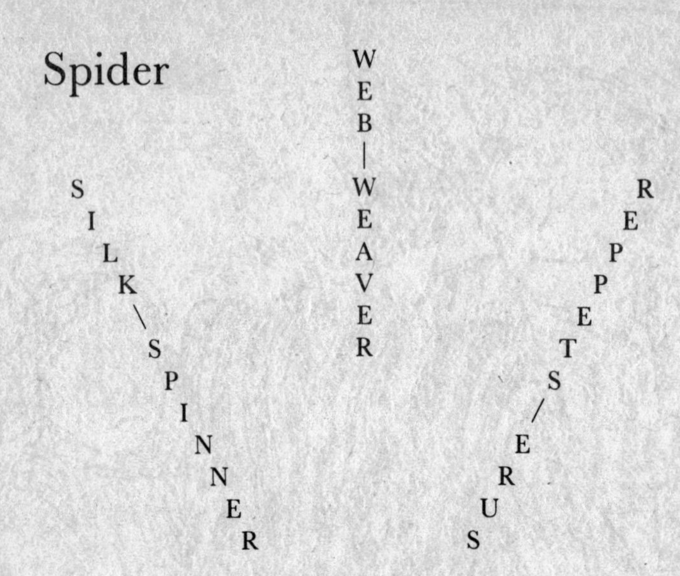

FLY—TRAPPER EIGHT—LEGGER

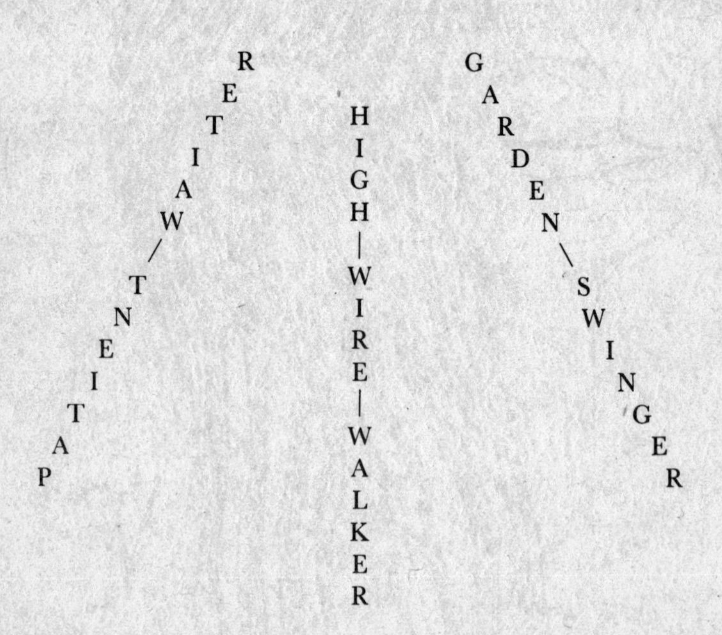

Double Trouble

Sometimes I'm called Katie,
Sometimes I'm called Anne,
This is because most people
Don't know who I am.

It's nice to have a sister,
But the cause of all the trouble
Is I am just like Katie
And Katie is my double.

My uncle says: 'I bet it's fun
Pretending you're each other!'
My aunty wishes one of us
Had been the other's brother!

It's not much fun when my friend Jill
Comes round to have her tea –
She sometimes plays with Katie
Thinking that it's me!

My mum knows what to call me,
My grandad's almost sure
And now there's a way of knowing
We haven't had before,

Katie's lost her two front teeth
So all she has to do
Is smile and grin at everyone –
Then they know who's who!

Growing

From
A seed,
An acorn,
Dropped by a jay,
Warmed by spring sunshine
Grew a tall, strong sapling
Spreading its leafy branches
Year after year, ever further,
Ever higher. Stately as a church
This giant oak, defying storm and cold,
Twenty metres high, two hundred winters old.

Snow in June

The soft snow falls
A swirling out-of-season scene,
The soft snow falls,
Past hollyhocks on red-brick walls,
On apple trees and lawns of green
Where shade and sunlight should have been,
The soft snow falls.

Waiting in the Wings

Why am I never chosen?
Why am I never allowed
To wash up the paint-pots,
To sharpen the pencils?
Why am I always one of the crowd?

There must be something I'm good at,
Pardon – what did you say?
Would I like to be King
And dress up and sing
In this year's Nativity play?

Oh yes, I am sure I would like to,
And yes, I can sing on my own,
I'll remember my part,
I'll learn it by heart,
Just wait till I tell them at home!

On With the Show!

We've made the puppets and written the play,
Sooty and Sweep on a Windy Day,
We've painted the posters, had lots of fun,
But will anyone come?

We've thought of refreshments, we've baked
  some tarts,
We've practised the play, we all know our parts,
The costumes are sewn, the scenery's done,
But will anyone come?

We've poured out the orange juice, 2p a cup,
We've set out the classroom and tidied it up,
The programmes are printed, and playtime's begun,
But has anyone come?

They're here! They've arrived! There's a queue at the door,
Twenty or thirty, fifty or more,
'5p a ticket for Children in Need,
Please take your seats with all possible speed,
Welcome to Sooty – we're ready to go,
Ladies and Gentlemen – ON WITH THE SHOW!'

Personal Statement

I am quite good at drawing,
I used to draw all the usual –
Houses, flowers, trees,
But now I can draw horses.

I am getting better at swimming.
I can do breast-stroke, front crawl,
And I am learning to dive.
I can draw horses in a stable.

I like reading. I can read books
With ninety-six pages. I like maths,
I can remember what to do.
I can draw horses in a field.

I am good at stories and poems.
I can write stories which have
A beginning, a middle and an end.
Here is a horse in his stable,

I have drawn him looking happy,
He is waiting to go out,
He is waiting to go out into the field
To roll in the soft grass and gallop.

Visiting

Grandad's in the hospital,
He's had a nasty fall,
He was standing on a ladder
To paint his bedroom wall,
When he thought he'd do the ceiling
And he stretched too far and missed,
And now he's in the hospital
To mend his broken wrist.

I went to see him yesterday,
I wondered how he'd be,
I'm not too keen on hospitals,
They really worry me,
But there was Grandad smiling,
Sitting in his chair,
Puffing at his pipe as if
He really liked it there!

'They seem to think I'm wonderful
To manage on my own,
They can't believe I'm eighty-two
And decorate my home,
They'd like to keep me longer
But I've got things to do,
After all,' he said and grinned, 'I'm only
Visiting – like you!'

Goal!

'Goal!' I shouted.
'Missed,' said my brother.
'Just a minute,' said Dad.
'How did that hole get into that fence?'
'He did it,' said my brother.

'Blabbermouth,' I said
As we went upstairs.
'It wasn't a goal,' yelled my brother.
So I lifted my foot –
'This is,' I shouted. 'Goal!'

But my brother had slammed the door.
'Missed!' he yelled from the other side.
So my kick hit the door.
My foot made a hole
Right through the door.

So now we are in bed
And I am waiting,
Wondering what I am going to say
When my dad thunders:
'How did this hole get into this door?'

And my brother isn't saying anything
Yet.

Eggs-actly

Eggs go with bacon or sit upon steaks,
Or disappear into custard and cakes,
Some eggs turn up in unusual places,
Pickled in jars, or in egg-and-spoon races.

Scotch eggs hide in a sausage-meat coat,
Fried eggs slide and slip down your throat,
I like them poached or scrambled on toast,
But this is the way that I like them the most:

Mix them with milk and flour and beat them,
Pop in a pan and toss them and eat them
Sprinkled with lemon and sugar – and then
Do the same all over again . . .

For eggs in a pancake turn out to be
Delicious – EGGS-ACTLY what's needed for
 tea!

Rise and Shine

I am usually late.
This is because I hate
Getting up in the morning –

But there is a time
When I rise and shine –

Every week
I'm out to play
EARLY
On a Saturday!

Finding a Friend

'Will you be my friend?'
said the rubbish to the river.
'No, never.'

'Will you be my friend?'
said the spider to the fly.
'Not I.'

‘Will you be my friend?’
said the lion to the deer.
‘No fear.’

‘Will you be my friend?’
said the boat to the sea.
‘Maybe.’

‘Will you be my friend?’
said the child to the summer days.
‘Always.’

Fair's Fair

When my little sister
Comes into my room,
I tell her to go.

'No,' she says.
'I don't have to.'

'If you don't,' I say,
'I'll tell Mum.'

'It's a free world,' she says.

'Well, if it's a free world,
I'll go and play in your room.'

It always works.

'It's not fair,' she shouts,
As she stamps out.

Giant

There's a giant in our classroom,
He comes from far away,
We've made him warm and comfortable,
We're hoping that he'll stay.

He wears a suit of armour
To shield him from attack,
It's hard to tell which part of him
Is front and which is back.

He keeps himself inside himself
Until he moves about
When eyes and head and everything
Gently ripple out.

His giant foot begins to spread,
His giant eyes explore,
And when he's eaten all there is
He looks around for more.

He waves his giant feelers,
He leaves a giant trail,
I never tire of watching
Our Giant African Snail!

Out in the Playground
(a sing-along and whistle song)

Out in the playground
Early in the morning,
See the children standing
All in a row,
Along comes a teacher
Blows upon a whistle
Whee-ee-ee-ee!
And in they go.

Out in the playground
Later in the morning,
See the children standing
All in a row,
Waiting for the teacher
To start the running races
Whee-ee-ee-ee!
And off they go.

Out in the playground
After school is over,
See the children standing
All in a row,
Watching the netball
There's the final whistle
Whee-ee-ee-ee!
And home they go.

Out in the playground
Now the day is over,
See the puppy standing
Watering a rose,
Along comes his owner
Calls him over to her
Whee-ee! Whee-ee!
And off he goes.

Friend-Lee

All my friends
Have names
Like me.

There's
Lee C.
Lee P.
Lee D.
Lee T.

And me
Lee B.

My mum says
I'm just Lee.

But
My teacher says,
'Come here, Lee B.'

That's me.

LEE
LEE

Best Wishes

Dear Mrs Matthews,

This is just to say 'Goodbye' and thank you
For trying to teach me a thing or two.

I know I haven't always been the perfect pupil –
But I really thought that time
When the gerbil escaped,
That I had fastened its cage,
And I certainly did not mean to get the whole class
Involved in the chase –

And I only painted your desk
To cheer you up. I thought a spot
Of Brilliant-Red would help your headaches,
And I still think painting all our desks
To match brightened up the whole classroom.

By the way, about me getting lost
That day we went to the Wildlife Park,
I honestly can't remember what I did to the lion,
I only know it chased me up that tree
And once there, it didn't want me to get down.

Anyway, I think you've tried
To do your best for me.

I hope you like the pad and pen,
Best wishes for the future,
Ken.

PS I'm really writing this letter for a
competition,
First prize – a bike and if I win
I'll bring it in to show you.
Thanks again. Ken.

Perhaps

Perhaps I'll go exploring and charter unknown
seas,
Discover desert islands, travel where I please,
I'll use the stars to steer by and land on foreign
quays,
Perhaps I'll see some humming-birds, macaws or
chimpanzees,
I'd like to see koala bears in eucalyptus trees,
I'd like to find a special plant and cure a rare
disease . . .

Perhaps I'll be a football star, yes, that would be
my aim,

Shooting seven goals a match would surely bring
me fame,
I know I'll have to practise, I know I'll have to
train,
Perhaps I'll play in Mexico or Italy or Spain,
I'd like to play at Wembley in an International
game,
I'd like to think that one day, the world would
know my name . . .

It's hard to know what's best to do or who it's
best to be,
So, for the moment anyway, perhaps I'll just be
me.

A Working Week

Monday mowed the lawn,
Tuesday tidied the toys away,
Wednesday washed the clothes,
Thursday threw the rubbish away,
Friday fried the fish,
The shopping was done by Saturday,
Sunday smiled and thought it was best
To work very hard at having a rest.

Sunset

the sun
is having its last fling
of the day
tossing bright streamers
across the sky
ruffling the clouds
into ripples of pink
refusing to go in

until

promising to be back tomorrow
it slips behind the trees
beyond the sea of darkening fields.

Hanging On

The wind is niggling that leaf,
Wiggling it,
Twisting it this way and that,
Like my tongue is twisting
My loose tooth,

The wind is teasing that leaf,
Easing it,
Turning it this way and that,
Like my tongue is turning
My loose tooth,

Oh, it's hanging on all right,
Stubborn,
Not wanting to let go,

One good push would do it,
One good hard shove – OUCH

Mum, Mum, my tooth's come out!

Newsflash

There has been a disaster
At the Magic Show.

Rosalie was cut in half
And looks likely to remain so.

We understand that the magician responsible
Is not available for comment,
As he seems to have vanished
Along with his doves, magic wand
And sixteen coloured handkerchiefs.

A white rabbit, however,
Is being held for questioning.

Rosalie is said to be
Putting a brave face on it
Which is not easy
When she hasn't a leg to stand on.

If anyone can supply
Human super-glue
Invisible sticky-tape
Or the whereabouts of the missing magician,
The police, not to mention Rosalie,
Will be delighted to hear from them.

Shelf-pity

I'm a book-shelf,
Not a dump-shelf.

I'll collapse under the strain,
I know I will.

The clock's all right, the piggy bank,
Even the lamp,
They fit beside the books.

But not rubbish,
Bottles of this, tins of that, a telescope,
Ornaments, marbles, rocks –

I mean, who in their right mind

Would put a collection of rocks
On a book-shelf?

I'm constantly weighed down with worry.

Every week something gets added,
A chess-set here, a football there,
A keyboard balanced on *My BIG Book of Jokes.*

I can't bear it.

You're not going to put that television . . .
Don't.
Don't even think of it –

I told you . . . I did tell you . . .

To Catch a Leaf

To catch a leaf, or so they say,
Will mean you have a happy day,
But now that autumn's nearly gone
And I've not caught a single one,
I don't believe the saying's true –
Still, next year, I'll know what to do:
As soon as leaves begin to fall,
I'll stand upon our garden wall
And as they're floating past my eyes,
That's when I'll take them by surprise,
And if I'm quick, I'm bound to get
A million in my fishing-net!

GOING . . . going . . . *gone*

CALLING ALL STARLINGS,
CALLING ALL STARLINGS,

BREAD FOR THE TAKING
YESTERDAY'S BAKING,

FLY DOWN THERE STRAIGHT AWAY
EAT-IN OR TAKE-AWAY,

CALLING ALL STARLINGS,
CALLING ALL STARLINGS.

calling all sparrows,
calling all sparrows,

peck up a bargain
clean up the garden,

crusts only left now
tell all your friends now,

calling all sparrows,
calling all sparrows.

calling a field-mouse . . .

This is the Day

This is the sort of day
I should like to wrap
In shiny silver paper
And only open when it's raining,

This is the sort of day
I should like to hide
In a secret drawer to which
Only I have the key,

This is the sort of day
I should like to hang
At the back of the wardrobe
To keep me warm when winter comes,

This is the day
I should like to last for ever,

This is my birthday.

The Christmas-tree Fairy

Here I am at the top of the tree,
Not as young as I used to be,
But doing my best – even if
My wings are torn and my joints are stiff
And my head is almost touching the ceiling –
To radiate the Christmas feeling.

This year they've put me out in the hall,
Squashed in the corner, close to the wall,
And a fearful draught from under the door
Keeps wafting my wand down to the floor.
Now, they've tied it on to my hand
With a far-too-tight, far-too-strong brown rubber
band.

Last year, I thought they'd gone a bit far
When the eldest child wanted to put up a star!
But the father said, 'Yes, I know she looks jaded,
Her hair's lost its silver, her white dress has
faded,
Her wings aren't so golden, her wand's a bit
worn,
But we bought that fairy the year you were
born!'

So here I am at the top of the tree,
Not the most comfortable place to be –
No one knows how the pine needles prickle,
No one would guess how the tinsel can tickle –
But while I'm up here, I know my place
And nothing can alter the smile on my face!

New Year Resolutions

This year I am definitely going to:
work very hard at school
keep my bedroom tidy
pull my shoulders back
AND
remember to take the dog for a walk
EVERY MORNING . . .

This year I am definitely going to:
stop biting my nails
stop eating too many sweets
stop chewing my lip
AND
remember to practise my trumpet
EVERY EVENING . . .

This year I am definitely going to:
stop picking on my little brother
stop teasing the budgie
stop pestering my mum and dad
AND
remember to clean my rabbit hutch out
EVERY WEEKEND . . .

There's only one more resolution
Now I've checked and read right
through them,
THIS YEAR I am definitely going to:
DO them!

When Winter Comes

In summer, when I cross the fields,
The grass is rich and green,
There's dips and hollows where I walk
And hillocks in between.

And high on top, a hill begins
Beside the hawthorn hedge,
A hill that falls with dips and bumps
To reach the river's edge.

In winter, when the snow has fallen
Softly in the night,
Each bump and hollow disappears
Beneath a cloak of white.

I take my sledge and whistle down,
As fast as any train,
And climb back up the hill to try
Again, again, again.

My Best Friend

He is . . .
black all over
except for one foot
which is white.

He has . . .
brown eyes
and a long pink tongue
which is rough on my hand
when he licks me.

He can . . .
run as fast as a train,
eat his dinner in seconds,
and come when I call.

He likes to . . .
chase next-door's cat,
sleep in the sunshine
and bark at his reflection
in the mirror.

He is . . .
my dog.

The Jungle Sale
By

Oh, Baby!

Ever since the baby came
Life at home is not the same,
Of course at first he slept a lot,
Of course my friends and I were not
Supposed to *breathe* in case he woke,
And playing silently's no joke.
We soon found out why all the fuss –
The baby made more noise than us!

Then at mealtimes from his chair
He threw his dinner everywhere –
Peas and ham went whizzing by,
Soggy custard, apple pie –
My dad and I soon learnt to duck,
My mother said: 'With any luck,
He'll soon be past this stage and then
We'll all enjoy our food again.'

He's talking now and drives me dotty
Shuffling round me on his potty,
Wanting me to stay and play,
Repeating everything I say –
Still, though I'm not too certain
Just what it is about him,
Despite his crazy antics,
I wouldn't be without him.

Fishy Tales

Do you know if dogfish
Ever bite or bark?

Only when a burglar
Comes prowling after dark.

Do you think that catfish
Spit and arch their backs?

Only when an enemy
Suddenly attacks.

Do you know if angel-fish
Use their fins to fly?

Only when they're travelling
Across a starry sky.

Do you think that swordfish
Would get into a fight?

Only when they disagree –
Then I think they might.

Do you know if butter-fish
Spread easily on bread?

Do you know it's half past nine
And time you went to bed?

Penguin

Perfectly equipped for swimming, streamlined in
Every detail, see him speed through the water,
Notice how on land, he waddles like an
old-fashioned
Gentleman going into dinner,
Up and down he goes, flat-footed, slow. But
In the water he
Never looks absurd, this graceful, polar,
water-bird.

A Vampire Strikes

I love to watch the horror film
Very late at night,
I love to see the scary bits
When good and evil fight,
The thunder rolls, the lightning cracks,
And then it's really good
When vampires roam the countryside
In search of human blood.

You can recognize a vampire
Even in disguise,
By his ruby lips, his pointed teeth,
His gleaming, staring eyes.
Vampires come at dead of night
And if one comes for you
And all your blood is drained away
You become one too!

My little brother's much too young
To stay up late with me,
But still I like to share with him
The adventure he can't see,
So when I go upstairs to bed,
With one gigantic leap
I show him how a vampire strikes –
And then I go to sleep.

Twins

we are .... we are
very like .... very like
each other .... each other
except .... except
for one thing .... for one thing
I'm your sister! .... I'm your brother!

I Like Poems . . .

I like poems that rhyme
And I like poems that don't,
I like poems that puzzle me
And I like poems that won't
Fit easily and have a very long line in the
middle;
I like poems that are not too short
And poems that ramble on and on,
I like poems that think they are
A song.

But,
I don't like
Poems which end in a question –

Do you?

Down Our Street

Down our street lives a strange old man,
Heats his bed with a warming-pan,

Eats ice-cream in the middle of the night,
Reads in bed by candle-light,

Paddles in the gutter when the rain comes down,
Never, never, never goes shopping in town,

Goes out fishing if it's wet or fine,
Hangs his wellies on the washing-line,

Sleeps outside when the weather's warm,
Rides his bike in a thunderstorm,

The happiest man you'll ever meet
Is my friend Ben from down our street.

Catching Flies

My dog catches flies,
Well, he tries
To, only generally they fly
Up, up and away by
The time he snaps his jaws –
Even outdoors
Where he can get a really good run
At them, he misses. It can't be much fun
Always failing
Always trailing
One leap behind –

Never mind,
He really enjoys the chase
All over the place,
Yapping
And snapping,
Leaping
And keeping
The flies on their toes
And one day, who knows –
He might give us all a surprise
Especially the – flies!

First Day Back

It seems to me since time began,
It seems to be the rule,
That every teacher has to say,
First day back at school:

'What did you do in the holidays?
Write as much as you can,
Did you travel abroad this year
Or stay in a caravan?

Did you visit a stately home
Or walk in the countryside?
Remember to put in the details
So that I know you've tried.

Perhaps you went to the seaside,
Perhaps you stayed with Gran,
We'll call it "Holiday Memories" – now
Write as much as you can.'

Same old thing, year in year out,
And everybody knows
We'll have to write at least a page
Oh well, eyes down, here goes . . .

Holiday Memories

When I was on holiday
I went to Timbuktu,
I wrestled with a jaguar
And boxed a kangaroo.

I journeyed into jungles,
I swam the deepest sea,
I climbed the highest mountain
And a monkey-puzzle tree.

I chatted to a seagull,
I met a big baboon,
I floated on a moonbeam
Until I reached the moon.

I visited the planets,
I lit up all the stars,
I gossiped to a parrot
Travelling to Mars.

I sailed across the ocean,
I drove a Greyhound bus,
I rode across the desert
On a hippopotamus.

I heard a mermaid singing,
I fought a killer shark,
I grappled with a Grizzly
In a wild Safari Park.

I chased a band of pirates
Completely round the bend.
And now the summer's over
And so is this – THE END.

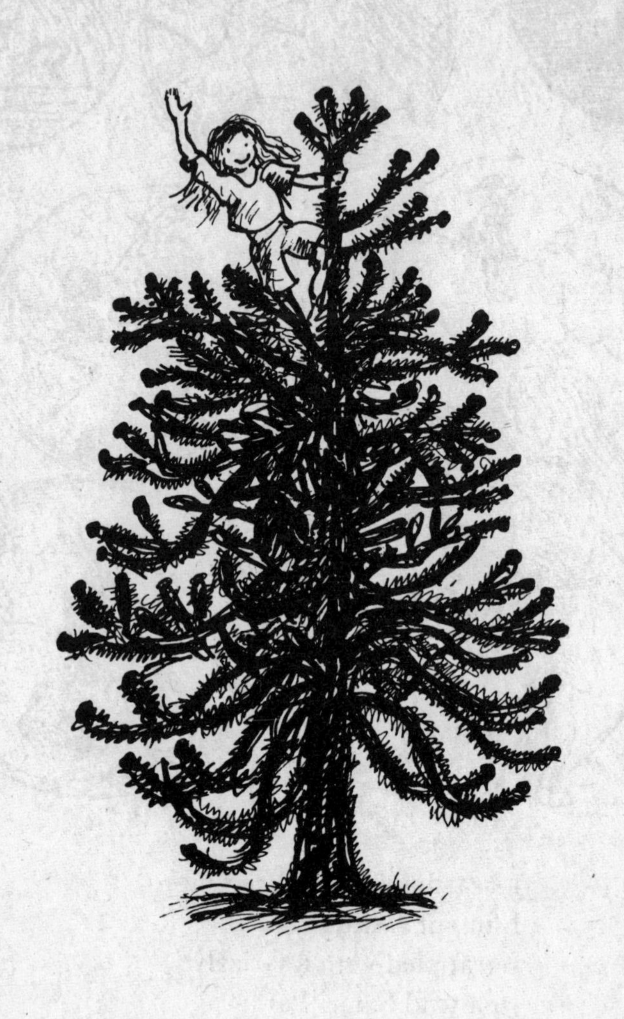